ToDAY was very special to George Washington for two reasons. It was his eleventh birthday and he was going to ride Firebrand, his colt, for the first time.

The events of this and future birthdays helped to shape the life of young George. He was to know sorrow at the death of his father, and excitement at the prospect of a career at sea.

With the skillful blending of historic fact and a gift for storytelling, Wilma Hays has written a unique, absorbing story of the early life of George Washington, first President of the United States.

Weekly Reader Children's Book Club *Presents*

George Washington's Birthdays

by Wilma Pitchford Hays

illustrated by Peter Burchard

Coward-McCann, Inc.   New York

To Anne

08-012

Library of Congress Catalog Card Number: 63-7739

Manufactured in the United States of America

By American Book-Stratford Press Inc., N.Y.

Weekly Reader Book Club Edition

The morning he was eleven years old, George Washington was almost afraid to open his eyes. He hoped so much that the day would be pleasant and he could ride, for the first time, the two-year-old colt his father was giving him for his birthday.

Yesterday had been blustery and cold. His mother, Mary Ball Washington, had said that no one could go outdoors in such weather. She had given each of the children a cup of hot bark tea to ward off colds just because his sister Betty had complained of a sore throat.

George slid out of bed carefully so that he wouldn't wake his three younger brothers, who slept in the same room. He opened a window and leaned out.

In the garden north of their red house were rows of yellow-green lettuce breaking through the ground. From the woods behind the house, birds were singing. To the south the field hands called to one another as they chopped off weeds with hoes to prepare the soil for setting out young tobacco plants. In front of the house a lawn sloped down to the Rappahannock River. George heard the clatter of men already at work on the wharf which belonged to his father's Ferry Farm plantation.

The air smelled of spring. George smiled as the sun broke through clouds. There was no doubt that he would ride Firebrand today.

George dressed quietly and went downstairs, through the long center hall and into the garden. He met the cook, Sukey, coming from her cabin to the kitchenhouse a short distance behind the big house.

"Mr. George," she said, "how come you get up with the sun? Gonna be awhile 'fore breakfast."

"I'm going to the wharf," he said. "Tell Peter to call me when breakfast's ready."

George had lived on all three of his father's plantations. He was born on the Pope Creek plantation on the banks of the wide Potomac River. When he was three, the family moved up the Potomac to the Hunting Creek house. George was almost seven when his father, Captain Augustine Washington, bought Ferry Farm on the Rappahannock River and moved here to be near his ironworks.

Each of the three plantations had its own wharf built on the river highway below the house. Here ships from England came to unload goods and supplies ordered by George's father. The ships also took barrels of tobacco and iron ore from the plantation to be sold in England.

Early as it was, men on horseback were waiting to board the flat ferry which traveled back and forth between the wharf and the town of Fredericksburg across the river. George knew that his mother thought the noisy public ferry was a nuisance but he found it fascinating to watch.

This morning a strong young man and woman were loading a bateau. The small open boat with oars had a homemade sail but they seemed happy to own it. George recognized them as bond-servants who had worked several years on a neighboring plantation to pay for their passage from England. Now their time of service was over and they were free to go where they chose. They had been married yesterday and were leaving for the western part of Virginia to settle land there.

The young man's friends were helping them load all the things they had to begin their new life in the wilderness: bags of grain, tobacco seed, carpentry tools, hoes, axes, a gun and a keg of powder. As they were ready to push off, the young blacksmith from Ferry Farm ran to the wharf with a last gift, four squealing piglets in a fishnet bag.

"Can't farm without livestock," he said.

George waved and called good-bye as the young settlers began their long journey upriver to Chesapeake Bay, then to the Potomac and downriver, through creeks as far as they could go before they must anchor their bateau and carry their supplies on their backs to the land they had claimed. George wanted to see the wild western mountains and valleys of Virginia someday but he didn't want to go as they were going, without a single horse to ride.

The blacksmith called after his friends, "Don't let old Fairfax scare you out!"

The young man in the bateau lifted his gun and shouted, "That for Fairfax's surveyors!"

George frowned. He had heard his father and his half-brother, Lawrence, talk about the dispute over the western lands. Lawrence said that Lord Thomas Fairfax of England claimed the wilderness as far west as the "first springs" and "heads" of the Potomac and Rappahannock rivers. He had inherited these lands through a grant from the King of England to his grandfather.

The colony of Virginia agreed that Lord

Fairfax owned more than a million acres of the Northern Neck, a strip of land between the Potomac and Rappahannock rivers, but the Virginia government denied that the king had intended Lord Fairfax to have the lands as far west as the "first springs" of these two rivers. The first springs went far back into the fertile Shenandoah Valley. Such a grant would cover more than five million acres of Virginia land!

Years of court battles had been carried on over this disagreement. Lord Fairfax sent surveyors into the wilderness. The government sent other surveyors. Each tried to prove the other wrong about the location of the first springs.

George understood how troubled settlers must be over this quarrel. Until the Privy Council made a decision, men didn't know whether they owned the land they filed on through the government at Williamsburg or whether they must always pay a rent to Lord Fairfax.

Sukey's boy, Peter, called, "Mr. George, breakfast's waitin' on you."

As George walked back to the house a horseman come over the hill. He stopped to see if it might be one of his older half-brothers. His oldest brother, Lawrence, lived on his father's Hunting Creek plantation and Austin lived at the Pope Creek home. George loved both the brothers born to his father's first wife, but he hoped the horseman was Lawrence.

Lawrence was fourteen years older than George but people said they looked alike, light brown hair, light blue-gray eyes and a straight nose. He had been educated in a fine school in England, the school George planned to attend someday. He had been a dashing officer in England's war with Spain, was wounded and returned home last year.

Lawrence was going to marry Anne Fairfax, the daughter of Colonel Fairfax, who lived on the plantation next to Hunting Creek. Colonel Fairfax and Lord Fairfax were cousins and the

Colonel was agent in charge of the Virginia lands belonging to the nobleman. Lawrence would be connected by marriage to all the excitement of the land dispute. George dreamed of growing up to be like his oldest brother.

George shaded his eyes with his hand to see the horseman better, but the rider turned and followed the lane to the ferry, just another traveler crossing to Fredericksburg.

At breakfast over Sukey's hotcakes with fried ham, Mr. Washington explained that Lawrence was in bed again with the fever that had come upon him in the war.

"But he sent you a present, George." His father smiled and reached under the big leather-bottomed chair in which he sat. He gave George a bridle trimmed with silver.

George felt the strong fine leather reins. "It's beautiful," he said.

"Happy birthday," his sister and brothers shouted and tried to give him their presents all at once.

Betty gave a saddle blanket with a red *F* on the corner. "I embroidered it myself," she said.

Samuel gave a halter he had braided. Little Jack and Charles gave red and yellow ribbons to braid into Firebrand's mane and tail. "Of course you can't use these until he's tame," Jack said.

George smiled. Everyone had known that he would rather have something for his horse than for himself, everyone except his mother. She gave him a pair of shining black dancing pumps with silver buckles.

"I do hope your feet won't grow any more," she said. "These are the largest gentlemen's shoes the captain brought from England."

George thanked her and placed the pumps on the table beside the gifts for Firebrand.

Last year on his tenth birthday his mother had decided that it was time for him to learn to dance. She had taught the children the steps to "High Betty Martin," "Leather the Strap" and "Pettycoate." During the winter George went to dancing school. The dancing master came in turn to the homes of the boys and girls in the class.

"No son of mine," his mother had told George, "is going to step on a lady's toes on the dance floor."

The colts lifted their heads and raced across the pasture. Halfway to the gate they stopped and snorted. They didn't seem to like the number of people gathered there. George whistled again, but the colts wheeled and ran away, except Firebrand.

The red colt came forward cautiously. Almost within reach of George, he stopped. His velvet nostrils widened and his large eyes blazed.

"What spirit," Mrs. Washington said softly.

George was pleased. His mother rode well herself and knew a fine horse when she saw it.

"George, do be careful," she said.

"Beautiful," Betty whispered.

"*Sh-h,*" George said. "Hold out the sugar."

His sister held her hand between the bars of the gate. Firebrand pranced sideways and eyed the chunk of sugar in her palm. George coaxed him with a low whistle.

The colt edged nearer and stretched his slender neck. Firebrand liked sugar. He was

also curious. He seemed to be thinking that the other colts might be afraid of all these people, but *he* wanted to know what it was all about.

The colt took another step and George's heart beat faster. In a moment he would be flying across the pasture on Firebrand's back.

George lifted the halter with the long braided rein looped around his wrist. When the red colt dipped his head for the sugar, George caught him high on the nose with one hand. Quickly he slipped the halter over Firebrand's head, back of his ears, and tightened the slip-knot around his neck. With his free hand, George clutched a hank of mane and swung himself onto the colt's back.

For a moment Firebrand stood perfectly still. George had time to see his sister and brothers smile, and Peter's surprised grin. Then he felt Firebrand's sides quiver. His father nodded approvingly as George tightened the halter rein with one hand and stroked the colt's neck. "There," he said soothingly.

Firebrand squealed. He reared on his hind legs. He pivoted, came down hard on his front legs and shook himself. George hung on with his knees pressed into the horse's sides and his hand firm on the halter rein.

Firebrand plunged. He spread his front legs wide and whipped his head between his knees.

George was jerked forward. He sailed over the colt's head and struck the ground. He was so jolted he couldn't think or see for a moment. Firebrand dragged him by the braided rein looped around his wrist.

George heard his mother cry, "Let him go.
You'll be hurt."

He knew the danger, but such a strong feel-
ing rose in him not to give up, that he couldn't
let go. He rolled over onto his stomach and
pulled on the rein with both hands. He bumped
along over the grass until his weight slowed
the colt, then stopped him.

George got to his feet and reached Firebrand's quivering side. He caught the mane
and jumped astride again.

Firebrand seemed to understand that he had met a will stronger than his own, or maybe he understood now that the weight on his back was George. He began to run. He raced across the pasture and along the bank of the river. The other colts scattered, then bunched in a corner of the pasture. George could see their wide eyes and tossing manes each time Firebrand carried him past them.

George forgot his bruises and scratches. He could feel the power of Firebrand's running move up through him. It made his blood tingle. The morning air was sharp and fresh against his face. He was having a wonderful time.

"Fine. You're doing fine, Firebrand," he cried.

It seemed to George that the little horse really cut loose then. He flattened out and tried to out-race the wind. He didn't mind having George on his back. He seemed to want to show the boy just what he could do.

When George thought the colt had run

enough, he slowed Firebrand near the pasture
gate. He slipped the halter off and let the colt
go free.

"You rode him," Betty shouted.

"You really rode him," the little boys cried.

"You sure did," Peter said as proudly as if
he had done it himself.

"You could have been killed," his mother
said. She brushed the dirt from his hair and
looked at the bruise where the leather halter
strap had cut into his wrist.

His father put his hand on George's shoulder. "The colt isn't broken yet, but the next time will be easier," he said.

George knew his father was pleased that he hadn't given up. His father understood that George had to finish whatever he had begun to do. His father was like that, too, and so was Lawrence.

As George walked back to the house with his family, he couldn't think of anything he would rather be than a planter like his father and Lawrence. When he had gone to England and had a proper education, he would come right back here. He would help his father plant tobacco and run the ironworks. They would hunt fox and game with other plantation owners. They would talk about good dogs and spirited horses and settling the western lands, when they went to parties at their neighbors' homes. George liked the way his family lived.

George never forgot his eleventh birthday. Not only was it the first time he rode Firebrand, but soon afterward his whole life was changed.

At Eastertime George and Betty rode their horses to visit their cousins who lived across the fields on the Potomac River. The cousins swarmed out of the house to greet them. Everyone on the plantations enjoyed having company. There were always extra beds and plenty of food.

A few nights later George and his cousin John were getting ready for bed when they heard the dogs begin to bark. They looked out the window. In the moonlight a rider leaped from his horse and hurried toward the house.

"Who is it?" John asked.

"I couldn't see," George said, "but he was riding hard."

There was a knock at the bedroom door and George opened it. Betty stood there in a long nightgown, her face smeared with buttermilk to take off her freckles.

"That was Peter riding Papa's horse," she said. "Do you think something's wrong at home?"

George didn't know what to think. His aunt came hurrying along the hall.

"Your father's ill," she said. "He rode out to see how the young tobacco plants are doing in the far field, and was caught in a sudden storm. He was soaked and cold and took a fever in the lungs."

George knew that people recovered from

lung fever, but he was frightened by the look on his aunt's face although she tried to speak calmly.

"We'll take you home first thing in the morning," she said. "Now get some sleep."

☆ ☆ ☆

Betty rode in the carriage with her aunt and uncle, but George didn't want to leave Firebrand. He rode home across the fields.

The sun was bright and warm. The pastures were green. He passed an orchard in bloom and sniffed the apple and plum odors. This was a day to feel good. When he reached home, he would open the windows of his father's bedroom and let in the smell of spring. That would help him get well.

George rode over a hill and looked down at his father's red house. Curls of smoke came from its chimneys and from the cabins of the field hands clustered beyond it. Carriages and saddlehorses were tied under the trees in the grove. He recognized the carriage belonging to the Episcopal Bishop.

Men stood in groups in the yard, talking and shaking hands. Women wearing hats and gloves stood on the porch. They waited as if there wasn't room in the house for all the kinfolk and neighbors who wanted to help when they learned that Captain Augustine Washington was very ill.

George bypassed the people and put Firebrand in the pasture. Slowly he walked back past the stable. In the doorway of the kitchen-

house Sukey stood with tears running down her dark cheeks.

George knew right then that he did not want to go into the big house. He wanted to run off someplace by himself and cry, too. But his mother was expecting him. He went in and walked the length of the center hall to the back bedchamber where his mother was weeping.   ☆   ☆   ☆

After his father's death, George spent more and more of his time in long visits at his older brothers' homes. Lawrence explained to

George the terms of their father's will. According to English custom, the oldest son received most of the estate.

Lawrence now owned the Hunting Creek Plantation, which he renamed Mount Vernon in honor of Admiral Vernon under whom he had served in the war. Austin owned the Pope Creek home. George was to have Ferry Farm when he was grown. But Ferry Farm must also support his mother and his sister and three younger brothers.

There was no money now to send George to school in England as his father had planned. He didn't mind much. He really didn't want to leave his family and the pleasant life in Tidewater Virginia. He wanted only to grow up to be a gentleman like Lawrence. There were things an English school could teach him which it would be hard to learn alone. But he *would* learn, he told himself.

Whenever he visited Mount Vernon, he would watch Lawrence carefully and listen to his brother's courteous, kindly friends, too, men like Colonel Fairfax and Mr. Mason and Mr. Lee.

A Virginia man worth his salt liked to sit around the fireplace after a good dinner and say what he believed to be right. He would argue, walk the floor, make a speech if he had to—to convince his listeners of right or wrong. There wasn't a wishy-washy man living on the plantations. George was sure of that. These were men he could learn from.

More than that, his father had told him that there were things a Virginian breathed from the air, beginning right in his cradle. George wasn't likely to forget what his father had already taught him: loyalty and responsibility toward his family and country, truth and honor to his neighbor, courage always, and courtesy to everyone.

By George's twelfth birthday, his teacher said that he showed a real gift for "figuring." He still had trouble with spelling but in mathe-

matics he studied far ahead of his schoolmates.

By the time he was thirteen, George was tall and strong. His reputation as a born horseman grew when he went on hunts with Lawrence and Austin and their friends. There wasn't a hedge high enough or a stream wide enough to stop George on Firebrand if anyone else could jump them.

When George was fourteen the talk up and down the rivers of Virginia was about survey-ing. In April, 1745, the Privy Council had at last decided the dispute about the western lands. It ruled that Lord Fairfax owned all that

he claimed, more than five million acres includ-
ing much of the Shenandoah Valley. Now
men wanted more than ever to make accurate
surveys of the land on which they had settled
or which they hoped to buy.

Lawrence talked of buying western land
from Lord Fairfax. He believed in time that it
would become more valuable.

Lord Fairfax himself came from England to
see his lands. In England he was known as a
fine horseman and hunter, and he enjoyed the
hunting in Virginia. He decided to stay and
build a lodge in the wilderness where he could

live and hunt, and sell or rent land to settlers.

Hearing all this talk of land and surveys, George brought out his father's surveying instruments, which had been put away carefully in the storehouse. He wanted to learn to use them.

Lawrence's neighbor, Colonel Fairfax, had a son, William, who was a trained surveyor. He was older than George but they were good friends. From William, George learned how to use a surveyor's compass, the tripod, and other instruments. With these he could run an accurate line to measure land.

George loved surveying from the first. He liked to work outdoors and he liked figuring, adding and subtracting distances. His neat careful reports surprised and pleased William Fairfax.

"You're a good surveyor," he told George. "You can help me measure Father's fields and your brother Lawrence's, too."

Although George liked surveying, he knew

that he was too young to be trusted with more than simple work. Yet he was tall and strong. He wanted to work at something to earn money. What could he do?

On his fifteenth birthday, George thought he knew what he would be.

Lawrence always planned something special for George's birthday. This year he invited Colonel Fairfax and William to go on a morning hunt. After an exciting chase after fox along the river and over the fields, they returned for the best birthday dinner that George could remember.

It started with oysters roasted on the half-shell over coals in the fireplace. There was roast duck and baked apples, preserves from the West Indies and peaches in brandy. When the men moved to big chairs before the fire and took out their pipes, a servant brought silver bowls of raisins, figs and nuts.

George felt full and sleepy but he kept awake. He liked to hear the men talk. Law-

rence said men talked after dinner to sharpen their wits. They often thought out their best ideas during after-dinner discussions.

"I tell you," Colonel Fairfax said, "someone must go to England with our next shipment of tobacco. I'm tired of letting English agents decide what price they'll give us for our tobacco, but set their own price on all the goods we buy from them. It's robbery."

"They take advantage of us," Lawrence agreed. "Last fall I sent the best leaf we ever grew, but received the lowest price for it. Much of the fault is with the ship's captain who takes our tobacco to England. The captain has to be the go-between. If he's a good bargainer, he can get us a better price."

"We'd better be looking for a captain who's a better bargainer then," Colonel Fairfax said. "I can't spare the time to go to England — not with all the claims to be settled with the men on Lord Fairfax's lands."

George liked Colonel Fairfax. The Colonel was friendly and kind and had always treated George as if he were as much a man as William.

"I can't go," William said. He was to be married soon.

George wished that he could do something to help Lawrence and Colonel Fairfax. He had an idea right then, but he didn't say anything until he thought about it.

His brother couldn't take long trips. Lawrence hadn't been strong after he returned from the war. But if he, George, could go to sea as a sailor, he could learn enough to become captain of a ship. He would know how to bargain with the English agents. He waited until his brother stopped talking to light his pipe.

"I'd like to go to sea this summer, if I can get work on a ship," George said.

Lawrence looked surprised, then smiled. "A sailor can grow into a captain," he said. "It wouldn't be a bad idea to have a ship's captain in the family."

"It's a good idea," Colonel Fairfax said, "if you're sure it's what you want. I always thought you had a real feel for the land, George. I watched you help William survey my back pasture. William's a trained surveyor, but you took to it every bit as well as he does. You acted as if you liked walking over the land, sighting and measuring."

"It won't hurt to try the sea," Lawrence said. "I think I can obtain for you a post as middy on one of Admiral Vernon's battleships. He'd make a real seaman of you. I'll write to him."

All spring George studied, went on neigh-
borhood hunts, and helped William survey
fields.

Finally Lawrence received a letter from the

Admiral. He would take George and he expected to send one of his ships to the river that fall.

When George went to Ferry Farm for the summer, he told his mother that he was going to sea in September. She was disturbed. She didn't want George to go. Both she and George were strong willed. They couldn't come to an agreement. For every good reason he saw for going to sea, George thought, his mother saw two reasons against it.

His mother wrote to her brother, Joseph Ball, in England and asked what he thought of George's plan. She also wrote to Colonel Fairfax. "I know George often visits your home and he admires you. Perhaps he will listen to a man."

Colonel Fairfax thought carefully about his answer to her. He decided to write and tell her exactly what he thought of George. Perhaps she would see that George could take care of himself wherever he went.

"Honoured Madam," Colonel Fairfax wrote to Mrs. Mary Washington. "Your son, George, is strong and hardy, and as good a master of a horse as any could desire. His education might have been bettered, but what he has is accurate and inclines him to much life out of doors. He is very grave for one of his age, and reserved, not a great talker at any time. His mind appears to me to act slowly but, on the whole, to reach just conclusions, and he has an ardent wish to see the right of questions — the intellectual conscience. Method and exactness seem to be natural to George.

"I presume him to be truthful because he is exact. I wish I could say that he governs his temper. He is subject to attacks of anger on provocation, but he is a reasonable person. Time will cure him of this vice of nature. In fact he is, in my judgment, a man who will go to school all his life and profit thereby.

"I hope, Madam, that you will find pleasure in what I have written, and will rest assured that I will continue to interest myself in his fortune."

No matter how many people his mother wrote to, George went ahead with his plans to go to sea. At last in September one of Admiral Vernon's battleships arrived in the Potomac. Excited and speechless, George met the captain at dinner with Lawrence. He didn't have time to make the long trip to Ferry Farm to bid his mother good-bye, so he sent a note to her by a servant.

The next morning George's clothes and trunk were sent on board. An hour before the

ship was to sail, he rode Firebrand across the
pasture to the Fairfax home to say good-bye
to his friends.

Colonel Fairfax had gone to visit his cousin,
Lord Fairfax, at the lodge in the wilderness.
But William was home and the girl he was to
marry was visiting there. Sally Cary was only
two years older than George and he liked her
very much. She was so natural, pretty and gay
that he never felt shy with her as he did with
most girls.

William and Sally followed George to the porch as he left. "I'll take care of Firebrand for you," William promised.

"Now you come back for our wedding," Sally said. "I'm going to save a dance for you."

As George went down the steps, he saw Peter ride into the stable yard. George stopped and frowned. Somehow he didn't want to meet Peter. He must have left Ferry Farm before dawn to reach here before George left. That could mean only one thing, his mother had sent an answer to his letter, a hurried answer, and George was afraid to read what was in it.

He ducked around the corner and went downstairs to the storage rooms under the house. The dusky rooms smelled of pickle-brine from the kegs of cucumbers against the wall. George had no light but he knew that there was an underground escape passage which led to the dock where his ship was ready to sail.

George found the dark entrance to the tunnel. He bent almost double to keep from bumping his head, and felt his way along the damp bricked passageway. When he came to the end, he found the heavy door closed. He swallowed. What if it was barred on the outside? He lifted the latch and pushed with his shoulder.

Luckily the door creaked open. But he decided to sit in the passageway until the small boat, loading supplies nearby, was ready to go out to the battleship. Once on board, he would be safe from Peter and the message Peter was bringing.

George squatted in the doorway and watched the men load. He didn't hear a sound and jumped when Peter spoke from the dock in front of him.

"Mr. George," Peter said. "Your mama sent a letter."

He held it out. George had to take it, but he didn't open it.

Peter stood waiting. "Mr. George," he asked finally. "You going to run away?"

George was startled, yet he knew Peter was right. He was running away. He guessed what was in his mother's letter even if he didn't open it.

"I could tell her," Peter said slowly, "that I got to Mr. Lawrence's too late. You'd gone. I don't need to say I found you and you *saw* her letter but didn't read it."

George dropped his head. He would soon be a man, but until then his mother had the final word in important decisions. It didn't seem fair of her to send a letter at the last moment. She left him no chance to win her to his way of thinking. He must leave on the ship at once or be left behind. All he had to do was give the letter back to Peter unopened. She would never know.

He knew he couldn't do it. The letter had reached him in time and there was no way to change that. With one of his big fingers, he broke the seal.

"I heard from your uncle Joseph," George read. "He agrees with me that it is a bad scheme to go to sea. You are not to go, George."

That evening Lawrence consoled George. "I've been invited to visit Lord Fairfax at his lodge and look at the 1300 acres I'm buying in the Shenandoah Valley," he said. "You can go with me. Some people think the old gentleman is gruff, but no one hunts better than he does or rides a horse better. You'll have a good time."

The trip into the wilderness was postponed for several months because Lawrence had one of his frequent attacks of fever. A few days after George's sixteenth birthday, the morning came to set out. George was first in the saddle. Firebrand was excited too. He pranced and tossed his head while Lawrence and William and Colonel Fairfax mounted.

It would take several days to reach the lodge. The men stayed the first night at a cous-

in's plantation. The second they camped deep-
er in the woods than George had ever been.

As they followed the narrow Indian trails
through the forest, George could scarcely believe that one man owned all these woods,
rivers, valleys and mountains. Lord Fairfax's
grant gave him even the "fish, wild beasts and
fowle of what nature or kind soever."

At a place in the forest where the trails di-
vided, stood a white post pointing the way to
GREENWAY COURT, LODGE OF LORD FAIRFAX.

William, riding beside George, said, "He

had the post set here to guide settlers who want to apply to him for leases and land grants. He asked me to survey the land so that he can lease it properly."

"It will take years to survey this wilderness," George said.

"Seven or eight men will survey in different parties," William said. "We start the first of March."

Lawrence and Colonel Fairfax rode into a large clearing. George followed them toward a long low building of split logs. There were dormer windows under the high ridged roof and great fireplace chimneys at each end. On the roof were two towers with bells.

William saw George looking at them. "The bells are to warn settlers in case of Indian raids," he said, "but there's little trouble with Indians any more."

George thought this looked like a comfortable place to live even for a man who was used to an English castle. Behind the lodge was a cooking kitchen, a smokehouse to cure the game, an icehouse, kennels for the dogs, stables, and cabins for the servants.

Then Lord Fairfax himself came from the house and stood on the wide porch to welcome them. Maybe he has fine English clothes hanging in the wardrobe of his bedchamber, George thought, but in his hunting clothes he looks like any man.

As George rode nearer, he could see the thickset nobleman's face. There was some-

thing powerful and determined in the heavy brows, Roman nose and deep-set blue eyes. George decided that he would not want to be the settler who tried to argue with Lord Fairfax.

The men rested after a dinner of roast venison, quail, garden vegetables and berry pie. George ate more than any of the others, but he wasn't sleepy or tired. He could hardly wait until morning when they would go on a fox hunt.

Before the sun came up, he left the large featherbed he shared with Lawrence, crept down the stairs and went outdoors. He followed the sound of hounds, who yipped as if they were eager to hunt, too. Lord Fairfax was at the kennels surrounded by a dozen beautiful dogs.

"Come here, Little Lady," the old gentleman called. He went down on one knee as the smallest of the dogs trotted to him, her tail held like a flag over her back. He scratched between her long flopping ears and talked in a low voice.

"Yes, you're going with us, Lady."

He saw George and stood up. "Lady's young," he said. "Been out only once before, but she has a good nose."

George nodded and squatted to pet Lady. She was red, a lighter red than Firebrand, but she had the same look of spirit in her big brown eyes. And for a small dog she had the largest paws George had ever seen. He looked at his own oversize hands and smiled.

After breakfast the pack of dogs was set loose. They circled the mounted men anxiously. The horses quivered, tossed their heads and pawed. They wanted to start the hunt, too. Lord Fairfax raised his hand and they were off.

The sky had turned gray, but to George the day seemed golden. The dogs led into a ravine where trees, sprouting early green leaves, grew along the banks of a wide creek.

Suddenly a white-and-tan dog yelped, the way a foxhound yelps when he comes upon

the scent of a fox. The pack took after him,
every hound giving tongue. Lady was the tail,
following as fast as her short legs would go.
George could hear her excited singing in a
higher key than the baying of the older
hounds.

He gave Firebrand his head and they took
out after her. Behind him he heard the hoofs
of another horse. Then Lord Fairfax passed
him.

The fox came in view, racing along the bank
of the creek. The dogs were so close behind
that the fox had no chance to twist and turn. It
was straight running for some time. It looked
as if the dogs would get him if his hole was
very far away.

The fox jumped into the creek and swam. The dogs plunged after. While they floundered in the icy water, the fox dived, swam underwater and returned to the side they had just left. He crawled out onto the bank and raced for the forest.

Lady, trailing, was the only dog not yet in the creek. She took after the fox alone, yapping wildly as if she had planned to outsmart the fox. George laughed as they disappeared into the underbrush.

It was several moments before the confused pack sensed what the fox had done. Then they were after him. The woods here were too thick for a horse and rider to enter, but the yelping of the pack told that the dogs were circling. They were returning to the creek. The fox must live on the other side and hope to reach his home, George thought.

The fox burst into view with the dogs right behind. Lord Fairfax led the chase. The ravine was narrow here. There was barely footing for

a horse along the bank of the rushing water. The opposite bank rose steeply.

Suddenly the fox leaped the narrow water and scrambled up the face of the cliff. The tan-and-white hound followed. It slipped, slithered back, fell into the fast water and was carried downstream. The other dogs raced along the bank upstream to find a safer crossing.

But Lord Fairfax rode straight toward the steep bank. George, behind him, could scarcely believe the old gentleman would try a jump

that looked so impossible. Yet he saw the horse
and rider soar through the air and land on the
opposite high bank. George's spine tingled
just to witness such a jump.

He was riding fast and he didn't hesitate.
Firebrand, too, seemed to think he could do
anything another horse could do.

George felt Firebrand gather himself and fly
through the air. They cleared the creek and
landed safely on the high ground beside Lord
Fairfax. George patted Firebrand's neck proud-

ly. Lord Fairfax glanced at him with a surprised scowl, then without a word galloped to meet the dogs at the upper crossing.

The pack found the scent of the fox again and gave chase. Moments later George heard angry baffled yelps and knew that the fox had escaped the dogs and reached its hole.

The hunt was over just in time, for rain had begun to fall.

Lord Fairfax lifted his hunting bugle and blew two notes to call in the dogs. While the men and horses waited, a chill wind began to blow. The rain turned to sleet and stung George's cheeks, and his eyes watered. The dogs came in, wet and muddy, sneezing and snorting.

Lord Fairfax stood in his saddle stirrups and counted them. He cupped his hand to his mouth and called, "Lady? Little Lady?"

"I don't think she was with the dogs when they crossed the creek last," William said.

"You all ride back home and take the dogs,"

Lord Fairfax said. "Get them out of this storm. I'll stay and find Lady."

"I'll help you," George offered.

Lord Fairfax didn't answer. George wondered if he had done anything to make the old gentleman angry. Lawrence winked at him and he was even more puzzled.

"George, go back to the place where Lady followed the fox into the woods," Lord Fairfax said. "I'll go to the upper crossing."

As George rode back part way with the men and dogs, his brother laughed. "The old gentleman never met his equal as a horseman," he said, "until you made that jump with him. It'll take him awhile to get over it."

As men and dogs went on along the trail, George started to search where Lady had gone into the underbrush.

Sleet had covered any tracks she might have left. The search seemed hopeless but he couldn't give up. The small dog would be wet and shivering. If she wasn't found, she might die.

Firebrand slipped on the icy crust which covered the ground. George knew his horse was tired. He got off and walked. There was a rustle under a bush and he bent to see if Lady was there. A rabbit leaped almost at his feet and George stopped, startled.

He tied Firebrand and pushed farther into the brush. He kept calling, "Lady. Here Lady."

At last George heard a bugle. This time it sounded several long blasts as if Lord Fairfax was trying to call to him. Leading Firebrand, George made his way back to the creek.

He saw that Lord Fairfax had taken off his jacket and wrapped it about something draped over the saddle in front of him. George looked closer. Only Lady's brown eyes and the tip of her quivering nose showed above the jacket. He looked at the old gentleman's thin ice-covered shirt and knew that he liked this gruff man.

George mounted Firebrand, ducked his head against the sleet and followed Lord Fairfax home.

That night the men had a real man's supper beside a blazing fire. They talked late about good horses, good dogs, hunting, and how things were done in Mother England.

When it came time to go to bed, Lord Fairfax stopped George at the foot of the stairs. "You rode well today," he said.

"Thank you, sir," George said. "I hope I ride as well as you someday."

The old gentleman looked at him quickly and changed the subject. "William tells me you've helped him survey. He says you're good at figures and exact in your measurements and records."

George waited while the old man's deep-set eyes seemed to be sizing him up.

"You have courage," Lord Fairfax said. "You endure hardship well, and you don't give up easily when you run into trouble. That's the kind of man I need on my survey. How would you like to work for me?"

George knew he ought to say something, but he didn't know how to express the joy in his heart. "Thank you. I'd like that," he said.

"Then it's settled," Lord Fairfax said.

While Lawrence and George were getting to bed, George told his brother that Lord Fairfax had asked him to join the surveying party in the spring.

Lawrence smiled. "I hoped he would when I asked you to come here and meet him," he said.

"Why didn't you say so?" George asked.

"Lord Fairfax might have thought you were too young, if I had asked him for you," Lawrence explained. "I wanted him to judge for himself."

George lay in the dark, too excited to sleep. How fortunate he was to have a brother like Lawrence. How fortunate he was to meet Lord Fairfax, who was giving him his first real job, a man's job. In a few days he would begin work with trained surveyors to map wilderness land. He would learn something new each day, not only about surveying, but of living in wild country without the comforts of home.

He knew this was an important step in his life. If he did his work exactly right, then men would know that he could be trusted to do greater work. And this was what George wanted to be, a man whom other men could trust.

The author says:

Historical facts are few about the boy, George Washington, before he was sixteen and became a surveyor for Lord Fairfax. We do know the members of his family, his friends, the homes he lived in, that he was an unusually good horseman, the change in his plans which came with the death of his father. We know of the deep affection between George and his older half-brother, Lawrence. We know that Lawrence, in his will, left George the Mount Vernon plantation.

We know that his mother refused to let him go to sea and that he became interested in surveying when everyone was talking about the dispute over the western lands.

These facts, plus the diaries and journals of other men who lived at the same time, help us to know the *kind* of life George lived, the life of a boy in Tidewater Virginia in 1732–1748.

It is also possible to see how his early life helped form the character of the man who became the leader of the American forces during the Revolutionary War.

The boy who loved outdoor work and learned to endure hardship became the general who remained with his ragged, hungry soldiers, who lived in tents through the winter at Valley Forge. The boy who had to finish whatever he had begun became the general who would not surrender even though many people thought there was no use fighting the strong British army any longer.

The boy who was exact in his work and could be trusted became the man whom the American people trusted and elected to be the first President of the United States.

W. P. H.